SUPERFLEX®

takes on Glassman

and the Team of Unthinkables

SUPERFLEX AIDEN

WANTED

WRITTEN BY:

STEPHANIE MADRIGAL

MICHELLE GARCIA WINNER

25 YRS Social ThinkingJr.

Superflex® takes on Glassman and the Team of Unthinkables

Stephanie Madrigal, Michelle Garcia Winner

ISBN: 978-0-9792922-9-3 (print)
ISBN: 978-1-936943-54-8 (ebook)
Library of Congress Control Number: 2009933790

Think Social Publishing, Inc.
404 Saratoga Avenue, Suite 200
Santa Clara, CA 95050
Tel: (408) 557-8595
Fax: (408) 557-8594

Illustrated by Kelly Knopp

This book was printed and bound in the United States by Mighty Color Printing.
TSP is a sole source provider of Social Thinking products in the U.S.
Books may be purchased online at www.socialthinking.com

This illustrated story book is dedicated to all the professionals, parents and students who have sent in their ideas and stories to our National Superflex Academy. Our Social Town is much brighter because of you!

While all children can benefit from the social emotional teaching that is at the foundation of Social Thinking, it was specifically designed to help promote social learning in neurotypical or neurodivergent children who have solid to strong language and academic learning skills who also have social learning differences (e.g. autism spectrum levels 1 and 2, ADHD, social communication differences or social anxiety, etc. or no diagnoses). However, mainstream teachers now adopt our materials for use with all students as they find them user-friendly for all.

25⁺ YRS! Social Thinking®

Recommended Teaching & Learning Pathway
for using *Superflex Takes on Glassman and the Team of Unthinkables*
and the *Superflex Curriculum*

3-Step Pathway for kids ages 5-10*

1

2

3

Use Social Detective first to introduce key Social Thinking concepts/Vocabulary to build social awareness.

After building social awareness and a social vocabulary, depending on the age of your student, introduce Superflex to teach about self-regulation toward behavior change.

Use Glassman (or any other Superflex story books or games) AFTER teaching the Superflex Curriculum to take learning on an individual Unthinkable concept to a deeper level.

If you're working with kids ages 9-12

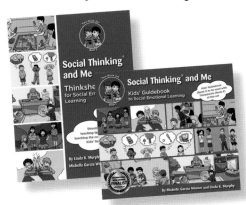

Start with Social Detective.

Next, Social Thinking and Me is used BEFORE or alongside teaching the Superflex Curriculum.

This two-book set helps deepen students' understanding of core Social Thinking concepts and gives them lots of practice to build stronger social competencies.

For kids aging out of Superflex (age 10+)

Start with Social Thinking and Me (if not already taught).

Next, move on to Social Fortune or Social Fate. (ages 10+)

* Some younger kids with social learning differences may need more time building their Social Detective skills. Wait to start Superflex with them until around age 8.

Find articles about teaching Superflex plus other books and teaching materials at www.SocialThinking.com

One Step at a Time!

Cautions and Information About the Use of This Material

Superflex Takes on Glassman and the Team of Unthinkables is book two of our Superflex series designed to help children learn more about their own social behavior and strategies to regulate it. As charming and captivating as Superflex and the Team of Unthinkables are to students, this is **not** a starting place for teaching them about Social Thinking and social behavior change. Social Thinking vocabulary and related concepts need to be first introduced to help children explore what it means to think social, to learn to be social observers and problem solvers, and understand the relationship between social thoughts and social behavioral expectations.

To be used effectively, parents and educators need to start at the beginning, introduce core concepts, and work through the Superflex curriculum **before** sharing this story book (or others to follow) with children. Books should be introduced in this order (see note if working with older kids):

1. *You Are a Social Detective!*
2. *Superflex... A Superhero Social Thinking® Curriculum* that includes the book *Superflex Takes on Rock Brain and the Team of Unthinkables*

Once these three books have been used with a child or class, adults are free to move on to any of the individual Unthinkables books we have produced to date, in any order that meets the child's social learning differences or interests. These books explore concepts in more depth:

- *Superflex Takes on Glassman and the Team of Unthinkables*
- *Superflex Takes on Brain Eater and the Team of Unthinkables*
- *Superflex Takes on One-Sided Sid, Un-Wonderer and the Team of Unthinkables*
- *Social Town Citizens Discover 82 New Unthinkables for Superflex to Outsmart!* (Introduces Superflex's Very Cool Five-Step Power Plan and the Thinkables)

In *You Are a Social Detective,* children are introduced – through child-friendly illustrations and language - to core concepts that make up the Think Social curriculum, such as "expected" and "unexpected" behavior, "school smarts" versus "social smarts" and other relevant concepts. Engaging lessons make social learning come alive for children.

Superflex... A Superhero Social Thinking Curriculum introduces Superflex, a Social Thinking superhero who helps the citizens of Social Town outsmart the Team of Unthinkables and diminish their powers to distract, disengage, and otherwise detour children in their efforts to think about others and use their social strategies. Fun exercises motivate students to learn more about how their brain works; concrete strategies give them tools to become better social observers and social problem solvers.

In *Superflex Takes on Rock Brain and the Team of Unthinkables,* children are exposed to their first Unthinkable character as they work through the Superflex Curriculum. This foundation of learning sets the stage for them to then move onto other books in the series, such as Glassman or Brain Eater. Each story book highlights a particular Unthinkable and its powers while teaching readers about strategies they can use to manage their own Unthinkables.

Adults can learn more about Social Thinking, along with additional teaching strategies, in the book, *Think Social* (Winner, 2005). Many free articles, blogs and information about additional resources can be found at www.socialthinking.com.

Note: If you're teaching Superflex to mainstream kids, or starting Superflex with kids a little older, we suggest adding another book into the teaching series: *Social Thinking and Me.* This two-book set, aimed at kids ages 9-12, takes a deeper look into core Social Thinking concepts and helps kids get the practice they need to integrate this new information into everyday functioning. See the Learning Pathways page for when to introduce it into the teaching series.

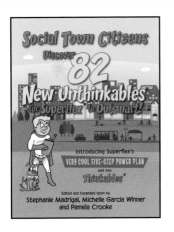

About This Book

In *Superflex Takes on Glassman and the Team of Unthinkables*, children become familiar with some social learning strategies they can use to help them manage Glassman when he uses his powers to challenge their good thinking (how Superflex would think) and make them have huge reactions, even to small upsets. Although the story introduces specific strategies, it is recommended that adults also explore the additional strategies outlined below and the references at the back of the book, which provide ways to expand discussions with children and students.

Not all strategies presented in the book will apply to every child. Caregivers and educators should closely evaluate what strategies work best for each child and encourage children to identify what strategies they do and don't like.

Additional resource related to problem solving strategies (introduced on pages 22-25):
*   *Think Social! A Social Thinking Curriculum for School Age Students.* M. Winner (2005). Social Thinking Publishing.

Additional resources related to calming strategies (introduced on pages 34-35):
*   *Exploring Feelings. Cognitive Behaviour Therapy to Manage Anxiety.* T. Attwood (2004). Future Horizons, Inc: Arlington,TX.
*   *Exploring Feelings. Cognitive Behaviour Therapy to Manage Anger.* T. Attwood (2004). Future Horizons, Inc: Arlington, TX.

Additional resources related to the concept of using your inner coach and positive self-talk strategies (introduced on pages 48-51):
*   *Helping Your Anxious Child: A Step-by-Step Guide for Parents, 2nd Edition.* R. Rapee, A. Wignall, S. Spence, and V. Cobham (2000). New Harbinger Publications: Oakland, CA.
*   *No More Meltdowns: Positive Strategies for Managing and Preventing*

Out-of-Control Behavior. J. Baker (2008). Future Horizons, Inc: Arlington, TX.
- *When My Worries Get Too Big! A Relaxation Book for Children Who Live with Anxiety.* K. Dunn Buron (2006). Autism Asperger Publishing Company: Shawnee Mission, KS.

Using the Series: Things to Keep in Mind

- Children who will benefit from the Superflex curriculum are those who can differentiate well between fantasy and reality. They are encouraged to think about and understand that Superflex is a pretend character, and should be able to imagine they have a Superflexible superhero within them that can help them identify and use strategies to change their behavior. This is a very different concept than pretending to be a superhero in a play situation. Pre-teach children that managing an Unthinkable is something that happens in their brains and is not a battle with their bodies. Children who struggle with these ideas may not be good candidates for the Superflex curriculum.

- The concepts in this book are best suited for students ages 8-11 with social learning differences. While many neurotypical students ages 5-7 will also find this material engaging and helpful, students of that age with social learning differences may find it too demanding too soon in their social learning lives!

- If students protest discussions related to the use of their own Superflex, please discontinue using this curriculum as a teaching tool and spend more time helping those children learn about the social world that surrounds them. Not every child is ready to take on his or her own personal program for behavior self-regulation and behavior change.

- The ultimate goal of all Social Thinking teachings is to help children become better observers of social information and improve their responses and related social skills.

Congratulations! If you are reading this story, you've probably been picked to be a student at the National Superflex Academy. At the Academy, you will learn how to become your own Superflex, a special kind of superhero.

You will study the sneaky ways of the *Team of Unthinkables*, who would like to take control of the thinking inside your brain and get you to act in ways that show you aren't thinking about others. You also will learn Superflex strategies that can manage the Unthinkables and prevent them from controlling your brain.

Part of your Superflex training is to get to know each and every one of these Unthinkables – in case you need to work on getting rid of them! Reading this story is one of the many fun things you will get to do while attending the very important Superflex Academy.

Along this adventure there will also be fun Social Town facts and quizzes to test your Superflex smarts. Possible answers can be found on the last pages of the book.

The Team of Unthinkables has been around a long time, invading and controlling the brains of the citizens in Social Town! In Social Town, people live together and think about each other every day.

In this story, Glassman and his friends will try their luck at taking over Social Town. All of the Unthinkables are pretty clever, and they find ways to combine their powers to control our brains.

If you notice an Unthinkable lurking on the pages and helping Glassman, you can help manage them by thinking of your own strategy or by looking at Superflex's Tip Sheet toward the back of this book.

You see, each of us has a Superflex superhero inside our brain. Superflex's job is to remind us to use our strategies to work and play well with others.

In Social Town last summer, the ever-sneaky Team of Unthinkables tried to take over by getting rid of Superflex and the Superflex Brain Sensor so that no one could use their Superflex powers. But Aiden and his dog Bark found the sensor, and now when the Unthinkables are up to their tricks, Aiden receives a signal in his brain and transforms into his Superflex. Superflex Aiden can remind citizens to call on their own Superflexible thinking to manage the Unthinkables.

Once Aiden receives a message about who needs help, he and Bark are off on their next mission to save Social Town! If they can keep the Unthinkables out of Social Town, it will be a much better place to live.

Before you read on, it will be important to learn more about Superflex Aiden and his brain powers! But hurry, because Glassman and his teammates are becoming more active in the brains of the Social Town citizens.

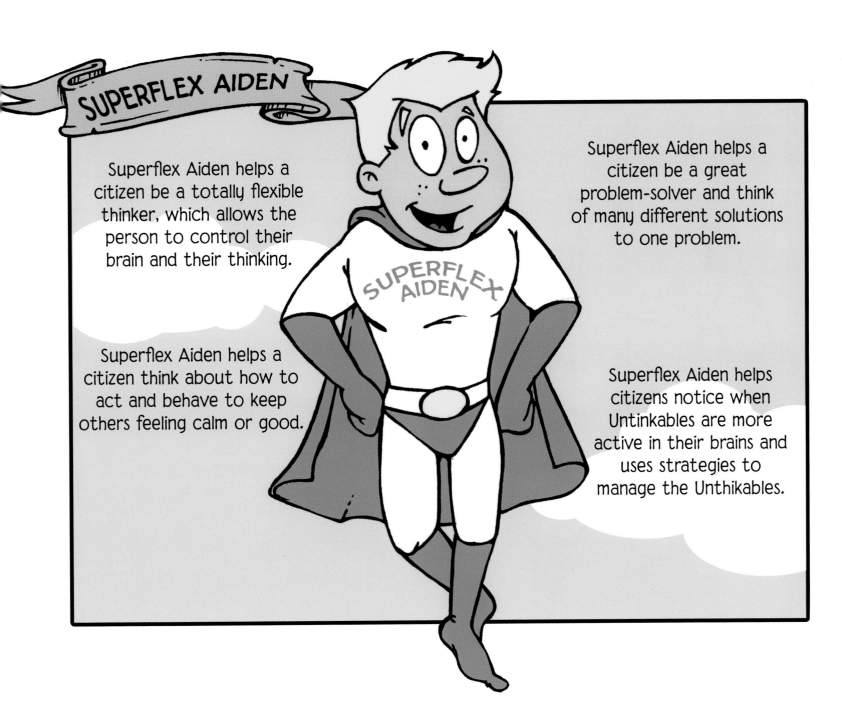

SUPERFLEX AIDEN

Superflex Aiden helps a citizen be a totally flexible thinker, which allows the person to control their brain and their thinking.

Superflex Aiden helps a citizen think about how to act and behave to keep others feeling calm or good.

Superflex Aiden helps a citizen be a great problem-solver and think of many different solutions to one problem.

Superflex Aiden helps citizens notice when Untinkables are more active in their brains and uses strategies to manage the Unthikables.

7

THE UNTHINKABLE: GLASSMAN

Glassman knows that citizens feel happy when things are going their way. But as soon as things don't, Glassman pops into their brain and makes them want to shatter like a pane of glass. That's why we call this character Glassman (sometimes called Glassy).

Glassman does not give citizens a chance to react calmly and gets them to have big reactions to over tiny problems.

Glassman makes everything seem unfair!

Glassman is one of the most common Unthinkables who can get into our brains. It's no surprise – just take a look at all of his powers! But don't worry; later in the story, you will learn ways to manage this character if he is ever active in your brain.

10

Aiden couldn't wait for the school year to begin. He missed his friends and was excited to tell them about his awesome summer. Well, he could not tell them EVERYTHING, because not many people knew that he found the Superflex Brain Sensor which made him the head of the Superflex Training Academy. Little did they know that he could also swoop in and help to "save the day" by teaching students how to use their own Superflex to protect Social Town from the Team of Unthinkables.

Aiden is feeling good because he can see that the citizens of Social Town are happy and thinking about each other once again.

14

You see, this summer Aiden didn't have much time to play with his friends or go fishing with Bark down by the lake because many citizens needed help from Superflex Aiden. Glassman was busy trying to invade the brains of Social Town citizens.

Superflex Quiz #1:

Have you ever had a "Glassman moment" and had a huge negative reaction to something that others thought was a tiny problem?

Aiden and his mom knew they had to tell his teacher and principal about his new Superflex powers, because he might need to leave class suddenly to help a citizen. They were very excited for Aiden and Mrs. Cruz agreed to let Aiden leave class if he needed to help a citizen. He just had to raise his hand and ask to be excused.

Aiden and Bark make their way through the school playground but start to worry when they hear someone getting angry while playing a tetherball game.

Superflex Quiz #2:

Which Unthinkable is helping Glassman?
Can you think of a Superflex strategy to
manage this character?

Hint: Don't forget about the **Tip Sheet** in
the back of this book.

Okay class, how big a problem is can be tricky. The only way you will know the size of the problem is to think about a bigger problem and how your problem compares. Here is an example: If getting bullied and hit is a big problem, then losing a homework project you have to turn in becomes a medium problem, and not winning a board game is only a tiny problem.

How you react should match the size of the problem.

A bully problem might make you feel really scared, nervous and angry, so the reaction might be to run away and get help from an adult.

A medium-size problem like losing your homework might make you feel worried or stressed, so a medium reaction might be to walk up calmly to your teacher and tell her the problem so she can help you problem solve.

Now, losing a board game seems like a tiny problem when we compare it to the two other bigger problems. Losing might make you frustrated, but since it is a tiny problem, then a tiny reaction would be to let it go by remembering that everyone has good moments and not so good moments and then say "Good game!" to your friend.

Now let's practice and see if we can work together and come up with some tiny, medium and big problems and figure out how to react to each of them.

Superflex Quiz #3:

Hey kids, can you help Superflex Academy students and make a list of different-size problems with them?

Good luck!

OK, let's get back to Social Town Elementary.

I'll tell him he played well, even if I am a little bit frustrated.

Aiden and Bark are happy to see that the student was able to use his own Superflex strategies to keep Glassman from controlling his brain. Now other kids around him are having good thoughts and want to keep playing with him.

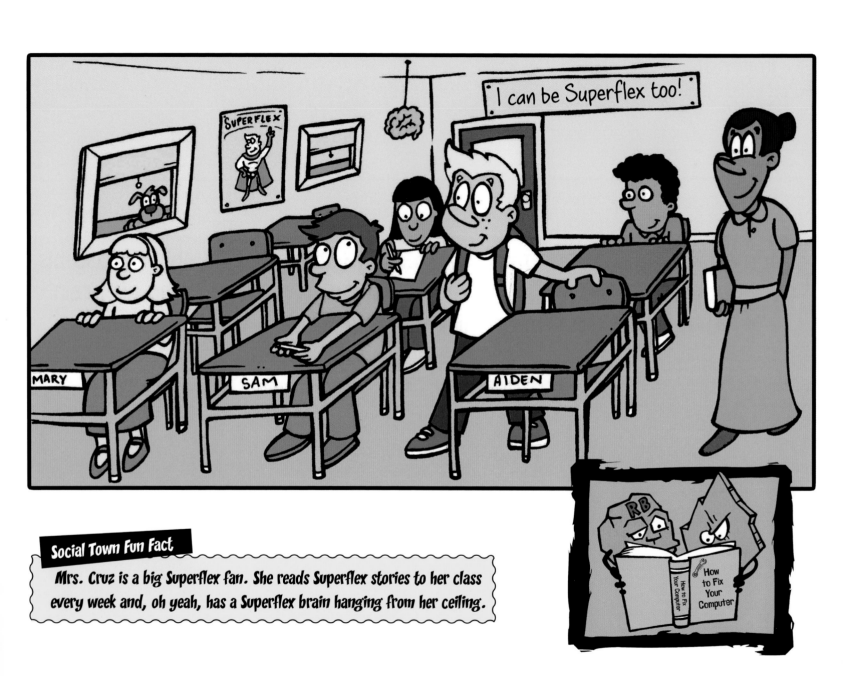

Mrs. Cruz is a big Superflex fan. She reads Superflex stories to her class every week and, oh yeah, has a Superflex brain hanging from her ceiling.

Aiden and his classmates are all finding their seats. Aiden is happy he gets to sit next to his friend Sam and be with one of his favorite teachers, Mrs. Cruz.

30

Just as Aiden sits down at his desk, he can see that his friend is starting to get mad. Sam is upset because his mom didn't put his favorite Superflex Jell-O in his lunch. The class is starting to have uncomfortable thoughts about what Sam is doing and saying because he is getting upset over a tiny problem.

A way to get your body to a calm place is to tighten up all your muscles and then relax them. This will help you stay calm and handle the situation with a better choice.

Now let's all try this: Make your body really tight, and then relax and release your muscles. Breathe in when you tighten your muscles. Breathe out when you relax your muscles.

Superflex Quiz #4:

Can you think of a strategy to manage Glassman's partner Rock Brain, who makes people get stuck on their ideas?

Use the **Tip Sheet** in the back of the book if you need help.

OK, Let's get back to Social Town Elementary.

36

If I'm upset, everyone will have uncomfortable thoughts. I can calm myself down: Tighten and relax, breathe in and breathe out!
It is OK.

Aiden is excited to see that his buddy Sam
was able to use his Superflex powers to manage Glassman.

Mrs. Cruz could tell this was going to be a great class!
All the students were following the "hidden rules" and thinking
about her as she started her lesson.

Superflex Quiz #5:

"Hidden rules" usually are not posted anywhere, but we are expected to know and follow them. There are hidden rules everywhere! For example, one hidden rule when you are in a library is that you use a quiet, whisper voice. An example of a hidden rule at home is that you are expected to be quiet when other people in the house are sleeping. By knowing and following the hidden rules, we can keep people around us feeling good, which will also make us feel good. Can you think of three hidden rules in the classroom and the ways people break them? How do we feel when everyone follows the hidden rules?

Aiden is listening as his teacher gives out the spelling words, when his sensor goes off in his brain. "Oh, no!" Aiden thinks, "The Unthinkables are at it again!" Luckily, his teacher Mrs. Cruz knows about his Superflex identity and that this might happen during class time. All he needs to do is raise his hand and ask to be excused.

Superflex Quiz #6:

What are the hidden rules when the teacher says it's time for a spelling test?

42

Mrs. Cruz has a feeling it is a Superflex moment, so she quickly calls on Aiden and excuses him. "Look out Glassman! Here we come!" Aiden thinks. Over the summer Mrs. Cruz was happy to hear that Aiden now helps the citizens of Social Town learn to use their own Superflex strategies to calm down the Unthinkables. Mrs. Cruz is ready to help in any way she can!

They find a corner in the hallway, and before they know it the sensor reveals the details of their next mission.
They are ready to take on Glassman!

This "inner" coach is inside your brain and helps you work through the problem, find the best way to think about it, figure out how big or small it is and come up with ways to handle the problem while staying calm.

But beware of the other kind of self-talk: "negative self-talk." The Unthinkables use self-defeating thoughts and negative self-talk to make citizens focus on how bad a situation is.

It is hard to solve problems when your brain is full of negative thoughts!

The Superflex Academy students were hard at work using their inner coach and practicing their positive self-talk strategies they had learned about in class.

OK, let's get back to Social Town Elementary.

Superflex Aiden and Bark find Room 3 and the boy whose brain is being controlled by Glassman and Rock Brain. Hopefully they are not too late!

Superflex Quiz #7:

Can you make guesses about what the students in the class are thinking and feeling?

Do they look sad, happy or worried?

54

The students are shocked and amazed to see Superflex Aiden standing in their classroom. They know Damane can manage the Unthinkables by using a Superflex Strategy. Superflex Aiden hands Damane a brain with a Superflex strategy on it:
"Remember, you have a different choice.
Manage Rock Brain by looking at your different choices. Manage Glassman by using positive self-talk. Tell yourself that breaking your pencil lead is only a tiny problem and you can easily solve it by getting a new pencil or asking your teacher for help. Broken pencils happen to everyone."

Superflex Quiz #8:

Can you list three self-talk strategies that would help you stay calm?

Can you think of another Superflex Strategy to manage Glassman?

56

Damane reads the strategy and uses his positive self-talk to help change his thinking. The class waits eagerly to see if he can do it ... and ...

Damane did it! He managed Glassman and Rock Brain! His classmates are so proud of him for getting another pencil and calming down quickly. "This was a much easier way to handle the problem," Damane thinks, and he will try and use the same strategy the next time he gets upset over a little problem. The children also have good thoughts about what he said and did. They all feel good about learning together.

Superflex Quiz #9:

What strategy would you use if this problem happened to you?

60

Superflex Aiden has done it again! Now the students of Social Town Elementary can get back to their school day. It looks like it will still be a great day.

Superflex's Top-Secret Tip Sheet to Manage the Team of Unthinkables!

GLASSMAN

ROCK BRAIN

Rock Brain: Take a deep breath and remember that you always have a different choice. Think about your choices, and choose one that helps others to feel good.

BRAIN EATER

Brain Eater: Turn your body and eyes away from the item that is distracting, and focus on what someone is telling you.

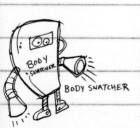

BODY SNATCHER

Body Snatcher: Remember to point your shoulders toward the group and keep your body about one arm's length away from other people if you are standing near them.

D.O.F

D.O.F., the Destroyer of Fun: Self-talk: "If I stay calm and remind myself that everyone has to take turns getting their way, then people call me a 'good sport.' Then others will want to play with me."

UN-WONDERER

Un-Wonderer: Create a "people file" in my brain about people I know. When I see them later, remember what I know about them and ask questions about what they like to do.

62

Space Invader: Use the one-arm rule to see if you are standing too close — which means you are supposed to stand about one arm's length from people. If you stand closer, they start to feel really uncomfortable!

SPACE INVADER

Grump Grumpaniny: Use your Inner Coach: "If I stay positive with my words, my friends around me will want to keep talking to me and will have good thoughts about me."

GRUMP GRUMPANINY

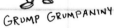

Topic Twistermeister: Listen to what people are talking about, and ask questions about what they are saying even if I really want to talk about my own interests.

TOPIC TWISTERMEISTER

WasFunnyOnce: Self-talk: "Is now a silly moment, or a learning moment? If it is a learning moment (most of the time in class), then I can keep my silly thought in my head so my teacher can keep teaching."

WAS FUNNY ONCE

Energy Hare-y: Look around with your eyes and see if your energy level matches those around you. In class, everyone's bodies are calm, so if your body is busier, take a couple of deep breaths to calm it down.

ENERGY HARE-Y

One-Sided Sid: When you are with your friends, try to ask them questions about topics they like to talk about. You can try to remember something they told you the last time you were with them and ask them about it. This will make them feel good and think that you are interested in them.

ONE-SIDED SID

Worry Wall: Find a thought that can change your worried thought to a calm thought: "Oh, this math problem looks too hard. But I can always ask for help from my teacher."

WORRY WALL

Mean Jean/Gene: Self-talk: "These bossy words might hurt my friend's feelings, so I can keep those thoughts in my head."

MEAN JEAN/GENE

Superflex Quiz Answers

There are many correct responses and possible answers to the quizzes you've taken throughout the book, so don't worry if your answers do not match the ones below. Superflex just wants to give you some ideas and choices to think about.

Superflex Quiz #1:

Have you ever had a "Glassman moment" and had a huge negative reaction to something that others thought was a tiny problem?

Possible answers: I might have a huge reaction when my mom makes me go to a restaurant I don't like, when the cafeteria runs out of chocolate milk just before I get up to the front of the line, or when my teacher tells me to put away the book I'm reading.

Superflex Quiz #2:

Which Unthinkable is helping Glassman?
Can you think of a Superflex strategy to manage this character?

Possible answer: D.O.F, the Destroyer of Fun, is the Unthinkable working with Glassman.

Use positive self-talk and say to yourself: I just want to have fun playing this game – it doesn't matter who wins.

Superflex Quiz #3: Hey, kids, can you help these Superflex Academy students and make a list of different-size problems with them? Good luck!

Tiny-size problems: A fly buzzing in my face. My shoe coming untied.

Medium-size problems: Forgetting my homework. Getting teased.

Big-size problems: Breaking my ankle. A dog attack. An earthquake.

Superflex Quiz #4: Can you think of a strategy to manage Glassman's partner Rock Brain, who makes people get stuck on their ideas?

Possible strategy: I think about the problem-solving scale to see what size the problem really is. If it's a tiny problem, then I just let it go.

Superflex Quiz #5:

"Hidden rules" usually are not posted anywhere, but we are expected to know and follow them. There are hidden rules everywhere! For example, one hidden rule when you are in a library is that you use a quiet, whisper voice. An example of a hidden rule at home is that you are expected to be quiet when other people in the house are sleeping. By knowing and following the hidden rules, we can keep people around us feeling good, which will also make us feel good.

Can you think of three hidden rules in the classroom and the ways people break them? How do we feel when everyone follows the hidden rules?

Hidden rules in the classroom:
Students take turns talking in class by raising their hand and waiting.
Students break this rule by interrupting the person who is talking.

Students sit and listen with their whole body.
Students break this rule by getting up and walking around while the teacher is talking.

If the lesson is boring, students keep that thought inside their head.
Students break this rule by telling the teacher her lesson is boring.

Superflex Quiz #6:

What are the hidden rules when the teacher says it's time for a spelling test?

Some hidden rules:
I quietly pull out my lined paper.
I write my name at the top.
I number my paper on the left-hand side.
I keep my body calm during the test.

Superflex Quiz #7:

Can you make guesses about what the students in the class are thinking and feeling? Do they look sad, happy or worried?

Thinking: What is wrong? That is a tiny problem. I don't want to sit by him.

Feeling: Confused. Worried. Stressed.

Superflex Quiz #8:

Can you list three positive self-talk strategies that would help you stay calm?
Can you think of another Superflex strategy to manage Glassman?

Possible self-talk strategies:
1. This is a tiny problem, so my tiny reaction is to take a deep breath and think about my choices.
2. I can always ask my teacher for help if the work gets too hard.
3. I can take some deep breaths. This always helps me stay calm.

Possible Superflex strategy to manage Glassman:
If I am starting to get really upset, then I can walk away and try to come up with a better way to handle the situation when I am calm.

Superflex Quiz #9:

What strategy would you use if this problem happened to you?

Possible answer: I would ask my classmate sitting next to me if I could borrow a pencil.

Hey Social Town Citizens!
How did Superflex Aiden get all those amazing powers?

As you read our Superflex story books you might have noticed that Superflex Aiden has some pretty amazing abilities to manage his Unthinkables. Just how did he get those superflexible powers? Were they magically given to him? Was he born with them? And how can each of us get those powers too?

Managing Unthinkables has always been one of the greatest challenges of all humankind. Why? It's because Unthinkables are sneaky and clever. Often they team up together to make us do or say unexpected things. And they're powerful—just when we think we've laid them all to rest, another one pops onto the scene! All of us (kids and adults alike) must always be ready to manage these foes, which means **we need to learn some extra powers of our own.**

Yup, just like Superflex Aiden did, we all have to learn about and practice our superflexible thinking powers to get stronger and stronger in using them. Luckily there's a special formula we can use when faced with any Unthinkable. This formula has been passed from Superflex to Superflex over the ages—it's **Superflex's Very Cool Five-Step Power Plan!**

Here's how the plan came about. You see, Superflex had five special pals: Decider, Social Detective, Brakester, Flex Do Body, and Cranium Coach. Each one had a special power to share with Superflex. As the Team of Unthinkables were gaining control of more and more of the brains of Social Town citizens, Superflex and his five pals knew they had to come up with some way to create truly superflexible thinking. It would require an organized plan, one with steps to follow so citizens everywhere could learn to use it too. So they created the Very Cool Five-Step Power Plan!

Superflex's Five Power Pals

DECIDER providers the ability to stop, decide, and describe which Unthinkable(s) is trying to overpower your thinking.

SOCIAL DETECTIVE provides the ability to stop and observe the situation and the people in it.

BRAKESTER provides the power to stop and think to discover the hidden rules (expected behavior) for the situation.

FLEX Do Body is all about "flex and do." He provides the power to use flexible thinking to figure out what strategies to use to do what's expected.

CRANIUM COACH is your built-in brain coach who silently gives you self-talk to use to get yourself through the situation.

Superflex Aiden learned to use the Power Plan and the more he used it the stronger his superflexible thinking powers became. Soon Social Town citizens were using it too, to manage those tricky Unthinkables and put them to rest. That's how you can get those same amazing superflexible thinking powers of your own! Use the Power Plan!

And, you know what happens when you do? **THINKABLES** start appearing to help you! What's a Thinkable? Oh, that's another story to tell...

So go ask your parent or teacher to get our book, *Social Town Citizens Discover 82 New Unthinkables for Superflex to Outsmart!* You'll learn more about the Very Cool Five-Step Power Plan and each of the 14 Thinkables that can help guide you in your learning.

As Superflex says, "Be strong! Be powerful! Be mighty flexible thinkers!"

Thinkables to the Rescue!

AVAILABLE NOW!

- Companion books to the *Brain Eater* and *Glassman* illustrated storybooks
- Help children compare and contrast the inner workings of their brain in tackling everyday social challenges
- Celebrate their ability to manage Unthinkables when they appear
- Use the Thinkables as a positive character substituted to shift attention in situations where students find it fun to only act out the negative powers of the Unthinkables

Preview pages from each Thinkable book and learn how to use these companion tools on their respective product pages on our website:
www.socialthinking.com

SocialThinking has so much to offer!

OUR MISSION

At Social Thinking, our mission is to help people develop social competencies to better connect with others and experience deeper well-being. We create unique treatment frameworks and strategies to help individuals develop their social thinking and social emotional learning to meet their academic, personal and professional social goals. These goals often include sharing space effectively with others, learning to work as part of a team, and developing relationships of all kinds: with family, friends, classmates, co-workers, romantic partners, etc.

FREE ARTICLES & WEBINARS
100+ free educational articles and webinars about our treatment strategies

LIVESTREAM EVENTS, ON DEMAND COURSES & CUSTOM TRAINING
Live and recorded trainings for schools and organizations

PRODUCTS
Print and ebooks, games, decks, posters, music and more!

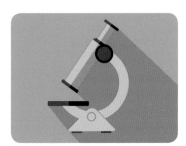

CLINICAL RESEARCH
Measuring the effectiveness of the Social Thinking® Methodology

TREATMENT: CHILDREN & ADULTS
Clinical treatment, assessments, school consultations, etc.

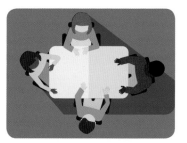

CLINICAL TRAINING PROGRAM
Three-day intensive training for professionals